KU-041-870

ADULT SKILLS Literacy for Living

Punctuation – Book 2

Written by Dr Nancy Mills and Dr Graham Lawler

LEARNING RESOURCES CENTRE
Havering College
of Further and Higher education

421

A.G

207711

The Adult Skills Range

The range of Adult Skills resources has been developed by Aber Education in response to needs expressed by tutors, students and governmental agencies. The materials are appropriate for adults who require support in advancing their literacy and numeracy skills.

Dr Nancy Mills, Adult Literacy/Numeracy author and editor, has over 25 years of combined experience in the adult education areas of teaching, tutor training, developing curriculum resources and publishing. Dr Graham Lawler, Adult Literacy/Numeracy author and editor, has over 27 years of combined experience in the adult education areas of teaching, tutor training, developing curriculum resources and publishing.

Adult Skills - Punctuation - Book 2

ISBN 978-1-84285-111-1

© 2009 Aber Publishing

P.O. Box 225

Abergele

Conwy County LL18 9AY

Published in Europe by Aber Publishing. www.aber-publishing.co.uk

Cover illustration by Michelle Cooper

Typesetting by Jonathan Bennett and Aber Publishing

Copyright Notice

The Adult Skills range of resources is produced for the Europe adult literacy/numeracy market. A Multi-User Licence must be purchased for each additional tutor using the same resource at the same site. Additional Multi-User licences can be purchased at any time. The copyright of this book grants the right for one tutor at one provider site to photocopy the activities.

For providers with multiple sites, each site is treated as an independent site and the above paragraph applies. The ongoing supply of these materials depends on tutors' professional good judgment and compliance with copyright law. This resource is covered by European and American copyright law, and CLA polices its use.

Contents

Introduction

General

This resource, Book 2 in a series of three, deals with the use and application of basic punctuation. It is written at a higher level than Book 1. Depending on the level of the student, it can be used following the completion of Book 1 to reinforce skills, or as a stand alone resource. Book 3 will follow the same format, but the examples will be at a higher level and the activities will be more challenging.

Book 2 provides:

- a progression of punctuation skills,
- exercises for skills practice and development,
- summary pages for revision and reference,
- blackline masters for multiple use.

Tutor knowledge of these skills is essential so that you can provide students with:

- focus and goals,
- modeling sessions,
- practice,
- feedback,
- purposeful conferencing.

This resource can be used for:

- individual or small group lessons,
- introducing and practising new skills,
- take home practice.

Lessons can be used:

- in the sequence they appear in the book,
- as starters for a focus on one of the skills,
- to collect baseline information for individual students,
- as pre- or post-tests, before or after the study of a particular skill.

These skills also facilitate the development of:

- reading,
- writing,
- self-confidence in putting pen to paper.

Using this resource

What is punctuation? – pages 7–8

Before launching into activity sheets on punctuation marks, it is important that students understand the purposes and uses of punctuation. If they don't know the term punctuation, they will certainly recognise some of the punctuation marks. The first step is to ensure that they relate the word punctuation to the various marks.

A discussion of the purpose of punctuation in general, with spoken or written examples, is relevant at this point. "Why punctuate? How does punctuation help us understand what we read?"

Once students have grasped the general concept of punctuation, ask them to think of all the punctuation marks they can and put one in each bubble (page 1). If they have trouble, you may give them some text

© 2009 Aber Publishing – Adult Skills   Punctuation - Book 2

and ask them to find some marks to copy into the bubbles. If they don't get them all, you may show them the ones they have missed so that they can fill in all the bubbles:

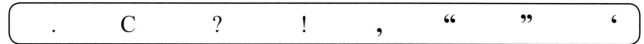

Ask questions so that you can determine if they have understood the importance of punctuation marks and are ready to move to their use.

At the completion of this discussion give them a copy of page 2. Work with each student as they fill in the blanks.

Punctuation – summary – page 9

This page has been included as a summary sheet or for use as a wall chart. It could be used:

- after the activity to reinforce the concept,
- after the punctuation pages and the 'What is punctuation?' discussion have been completed.

Note: This resource includes a summary for each of the seven punctuation marks introduced. They can all be used as described above.

What is a sentence? – page 10

This page is helpful to solicit the students' understanding of sentences. If working in a small group, ideas can be shared, accepted and returned to after the sentence sheets have been completed. The activity can be used as a pre- and post-test to gauge student progress.

Capital letters and fullstops, practice – pages 15–16

Use these three pages to review the concept of a complete sentence and reinforce the use of capital letters and fullstops.

The exercises can be used:

- as a one-on-one or small group exercise for general discussion. Is each one a sentence? If so, why? If not, why not?,
- as a follow-up exercise for revision,
- to correct the punctuation by putting in the capital letter or a fullstop, or both,
- to complete the idea to make it a sentence.

After the student has ticked the complete sentences, the activities may be used again by the students to make the other sentences complete.

More about capital letters, practice – pages 14-15

The purpose of these pages is to give examples of additional uses of capital letters. The activities will help to reinforce the use of all three concepts that have been introduced:

- complete sentences,
- fullstops,
- capital letters.

Capital letters and fullstops – punctuating a story – page 16

This page has stories with no punctuation marks. Ask students to make corrections to any or all of the stories. These can be used one-on-one or for small group activities. They provide an opportunity for students to discuss where and why sentences begin or end in certain places, and to justify their ideas. The groups can be of mixed or similar ability.

The summary (page 11) can be used in the same ways as suggested for page 3.

Joined sentences – page 12

Before students fully understand sentence structure and punctuation, their writing may be full of joined ideas using *and*, *then* and *but*. Joining sentences in this way is common for those who do not grasp basic punctuation concepts. Use this page with students to improve their writing.

Question marks and exclamation marks – page 13–14

The purpose of these pages is to get students thinking about other punctuation marks used in sentences and the reasons for their use. As part of the activity, they could either write a sentence that requires a ! or a ?, or find an example in a book or story you provide.

The activities give practice in recognising and using question marks and exclamation marks.

Speech marks – pages 21–22

These pages have been developed to provide a staged introduction to punctuating with speech marks.

• Examples of why speech marks are used are presented. There is also an activity that requires students to underline the spoken parts of a fully punctuated sentence.

• The idea of beginning each new speaker on a new line is introduced. Conversations are provided for the students to read and punctuate to show their understanding.

• The rest of the activities deal with the other punctuation involved in speaking and the placement of the punctuation marks that have been introduced to this point.

Commas – more uses – page 25–26

This section introduces the placement of commas in lists of nouns and describing words, and to indicate a pause in the reading. The exercises will reinforce this use of commas.

Apostrophes – missing letters – page 28

The use of apostrophes in shortened words is usually logical to students and easy to grasp. There are many practice activities.

Apostrophes – possession – page 29

The placement of possessive apostrophes is more difficult. It is a tricky concept and one that people of all ages find hard to use properly. Mastery will need time, revision and practice.

Apostrophes practice – missing letters and possession – page 28.
Examples and activities will help to reinforce the two uses of apostrophes.

Punctuation practice – pages 32–33

Here are some revision activities for all the punctuation marks covered in this resource. They can also be used as a pre- or post-test. An answer key for the stories is on page 34.

© 2009 Aber Publishing – Adult Skills   Punctuation - Book 2

What is punctuation?

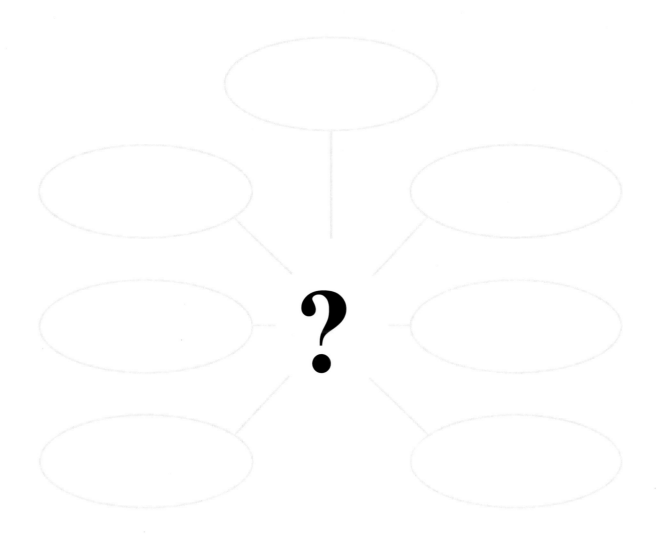

What is punctuation?

What do we mean by **punctuation?**

Punctuation is . . .

Activity

Fill in the gaps below by putting in the punctuation mark.

	A fullstop is a mark that shows the end of a sentence.
	A capital letter goes at the beginning of a sentence.
	A question mark shows a question has been asked.
	An exclamation mark shows surprise, excitement, alarm or anger.
	Speech marks show something is being said.
	A comma is used for a pause in a sentence. It is also used to separate items in a list.
	An apostrophe is used to show where letters have been taken out of a word. It is also used to show ownership.

Punctuation summary

Capital Letters

L M N W

- at the beginning of sentences
- at the beginning of names of people and places
- the word **I**

Fullstop

- at the end of a sentence

Exclamation Mark

!

- at the end of a sentence to show surprise, alarm, anger

Question Mark

- at the end of a question

Comma

, or **,**

- for a pause in a sentence
- between words in a list of things
- with speech marks
- to clarify the meaning of a sentence

Speech Marks

" " or **" "**

- to show spoken words

Apostrophes

, or **,**

- when letters have been left out to shorten a word
- when ownership needs to be shown

What is a sentence?

We know that **punctuation** is a group of special marks used in sentences. The marks make sentences easier to understand.

What is a sentence?

A sentence is a group of words or an idea which makes sense on its own.
All sentences have punctuation marks; a capital letter at the beginning and a fullstop at the end.

Activity

Each set of words has correct sentence punctuation but some sets aren't sentences because they don't make sense.

Read each one carefully and put a ✓ in the box if it makes sense.

	Makes sense
It made me laugh.	☐
I have six more units to.	☐
My car has a punctured tyre.	☐
That movie starts after.	☐
Please shift your car to the driveway.	☐
I have shopping to do at the supermarket.	☐
My new position begins.	☐
I like the options on my mobile phone.	☐
The Hurricanes' match is on Saturday night.	☐
Don't contact me before.	☐
Jacob's computer has a virus.	☐
I will collect you at approximately six.	☐
The book I'm reading is extremely.	☐
Last weekend the beach was crowded.	☐
The weather is too humid to.	☐
He chopped an enormous pile of firewood.	☐
My brother-in-law has a fractured.	☐
Her driving licence expires next month.	☐
That shop has.	☐
I can see the boat from here.	☐
My favourite show is on tonight.	☐
I saw Geoff in town at.	☐
When the thunder clapped overhead.	☐
The speed camera was set up on a long straight	☐

Capital letters and fullstops

A sentence needs three things to make it complete.

- It must make sense.

- It must start with a capital letter.

- It must end with a fullstop.

C	**capital letter**	All sentences must begin with a **capital letter**.
.	**full stop**	A punctuation mark that shows the end of a sentence.

The surf lifesaving club is having a meeting this Saturday.	**This is a complete sentence. It makes sense and has correct punctuation.**
I put my application.	**This is not a complete sentence. It has a fullstop and a capital letter, but it does not make sense.**
my brother bought a flatbed truck	**This makes sense, but it needs a capital letter and a fullstop to complete it.**

Activity 1

Are these complete sentences? Put a ✔ in the box:

- if it makes sense,
- if it starts with a capital letter,
- if it has a fullstop,
- if it is a complete sentence.

	makes sense	has a fullstop	starts with a capital letter	complete sentence
our rugby team is in second place.	☐	☐	☐ =	☐
We are going to gather at	☐	☐	☐ =	☐
Everything has gone wrong today	☐	☐	☐ =	☐
i don't know what to purchase for her.	☐	☐	☐ =	☐
Whenever I eat chocolate I get	☐	☐	☐ =	☐
the traffic was backed up because of	☐	☐	☐ =	☐
It took four hours to drive to Edinburgh	☐	☐	☐ =	☐
Eric is going to take me rock climbing.	☐	☐	☐ =	☐
I'm enrolled in an art class next.	☐	☐	☐ =	☐
the journal entry listed the wrong time	☐	☐	☐ =	☐
his boss fired him for arriving late	☐	☐	☐ =	☐
our library closes early on.	☐	☐	☐ =	☐

Activity 2

Look at the sets of words that were not complete sentences carefully.
Can you make changes to them to make them into complete sentences? Either add punctuation or add extra words to make them make sense.

© 2009 Aber Publishing – Adult Skills   Punctuation - Book 2

Capital letters and full stops – practice

Look at the sentences on the left in the box. Decide if they are complete sentences before you read the answers on the right.

The headlines in the paper were about the flooding in Westport.	**Yes. This sentence begins with a capital letter and ends with a fullstop. It is a complete sentence.**
Finishing my application. Returning home.	**No. These are NOT complete sentences. They have capital letters and fullstops, but they do not make sense.**
my flat is not sufficiently big for four people.	**No. This does make sense, but it needs a capital letter to complete it.**
Surgery is the only answer to my mother's hip pain	**No. This does make sense, but it needs a fullstop to complete it.**

Activity 1

Are these complete sentences? Put a ✓ in the box:

- if it makes sense,
- if it starts with a capital letter,
- if it has a fullstop,
- if it is a complete sentence.

	makes sense	has a fullstop	starts with a capital letter		complete sentence
We are rearranging our desks at work.	☐	☐	☐	=	☐
the administration staff need more room	☐	☐	☐	=	☐
human resources has the largest	☐	☐	☐	=	☐
put your pens down.	☐	☐	☐	=	☐
Everyone will wear old clothing on Friday.	☐	☐	☐	=	☐
my supervisor wants her own.	☐	☐	☐	=	☐
The new director is from	☐	☐	☐	=	☐
annual appraisals will be done in July.	☐	☐	☐	=	☐
salary increases are based on the.	☐	☐	☐	=	☐
I can't come this afternoon.	☐	☐	☐	=	☐
i believe that my results will be excellent	☐	☐	☐	=	☐
what will I do to celebrate?	☐	☐	☐	=	☐
Saturday morning I'm going to the swap.	☐	☐	☐	=	☐
Don't tell Jonathan that I borrowed his	☐	☐	☐	=	☐
Tell Mary I'll be late.	☐	☐	☐	=	☐

Activity 2

Look at the sets of words that were not complete sentences carefully.
Can you make changes to them to make them into complete sentences? Either add punctuation or add extra words to make them make sense.

Capital letters and fullstops – practice

Activities

Make each line into a complete sentence by

- **putting capital letters and full stops where they are missing and/or**
- **adding words to make each sentence make sense.**

When you are finished, read each story through. Put a ✓ next to each sentence to ensure it is complete.

Story 1

- [ ] my sister and her husband came to visit us
- [ ] we decided to take them on a sightseeing
- [ ] the first place we went was Rhyl
- [ ] the thermal areas were very
- [ ] they didn't like the smell, so we only stayed one
- [ ] next we drove to Chester
- [ ] two thousand years ago it was the site of an enormous
- [ ] the volcano formed a large crater which is now a
- [ ] while there we watched people go bungi jumping
- [ ] we decided to go jet boat
- [ ] the ride was absolutely fantastic
- [ ] that evening we had our final
- [ ] it took four hours to drive
- [ ] on their next trip they want to go further north
- [ ] perhaps we'll make it all the way to Scotland

Story 2

- [ ] my brother Amit and his wife have a new baby girl
- [ ] she is their first
- [ ] they didn't expect her to arrive two weeks early
- [ ] amit wanted to name her Nisha
- [ ] his wife wanted to name her
- [ ] they ended up compromising by naming her
- [ ] i think she looks just like my father
- [ ] everyone laughs when I say
- [ ] her eyes are the same colour as
- [ ] she is also very stubborn
- [ ] my father denies that he is
- [ ] we all believe that the baby is
- [ ] i'm really enjoying being an Aunty

© 2009 Aber Publishing – Adult Skills   Punctuation - Book 2

More about capital letters

All sentences begin with capital letters.

Capitals are also used in other ways.

Names of people	begin with **capital letters**.	Nelson Mandela, Jonah Lomu, Kylie Minogue, Albert Einstein
Names of places	begin with **capital letters**.	Rhyl, Wales, The Eiffel Tower, China, Heathrow Airport
Names of days	begin with **capital letters**.	Tuesday, Wednesday, Thursday, Saturday
Names of months	begin with **capital letters**	January, February, April, September, November
Names of streets	begin with **capital letters**.	Fifth Avenue, Towyn Road, Campbell Crescent
Names of businesses	begin with **capital letters**	Bank of **Ireland**, Telecom, Powergen
Titles of books, magazines and newspapers	begin with **capital letters**	The Bible, The New York Times, The Listener
Initials	begin with **capital letters**	H. T. Black, GST, HIV, SUV
I	**I** is always a **capital letter**	I don't know when I will leave.

Activity

Read these sentences.

Cross out the lower case letters that should be capital and write in the correct letter.

Cross out the capital letters that are wrong and write in the correct letter.

mr carrington is my science teacher.

i'll celebrate my Twenty-first birthday next november.

drop me off on mangere street.

i have to deliver a Cheque to TZT couriers on my way home from work.

my uncle was Elected as an mp for cheshire.

susan and jeremy are meeting us at the grumpy mole for dinner on tuesday.

we saw tom cruz's Movie the last samurai on dvd last night.

look in the yellow pages for the phone number of the information centre.

i have to apply for a national insurance number.

Deva university is hosting the first annual bathtub olympics over the christmas break.

i read an entire book called the hitchhiker's guide to the galaxy on saturday.

karen bought a used toyota supra from michael.

plymouth girls' high school won the stage challenge.

the top twins are coming to venue cyrmru in march.

my little Sister is reading harry potter and the chamber of secrets.

on thursday night we are going to stay at aj's house.

Capital letters – practice

Activity

Put the capital letters that are missing in these sentences.

Put a fullstop at the end of each sentence that makes sense.

If it does not make sense, complete the sentence by adding words and a fullstop.

carol and i are training for the third annual pepsi triathlon being held next december

my parents and brother darryl are in garden city

there is a used toshiba laptop advertised in the liverpool echo

the pta is having a meeting of all the parents at my daughter's school

please turn the tv on to the paul o grady show

i want the new u2 cd for

the eiffel tower in paris is a place i have always wanted to see

countdown is hiring packers who can work on saturdays and sundays

we can't shift into our flat until august

the video store is having a sale on dvds of classic movies

you should go to either fe college or sixth form for your A levels.

my mother has to have an mri at the hospital on friday

simon's wife is having twins by c-section on 20 april

hugh's address is 32 cooper court

the next gst return is due at the end of february

for her birthday i bought mum a subscription for

sky tv is having a special on their installations for the month of september

there is an interesting new book out about wwii

the usa has a population of over 140 million females and 134 million males

i'm looking for a toyota 4wd to rent for a camping trip in the country

my favourite movie is men in black

the interviewer rang to tell me i didn't get the job

nz is a country known as a destination for many european travellers

i was a member of girl guides for five

we had to show our ids in order to get into the club

some think that the golden gate is the most famous bridge in the world

my sister kay watches coronation street every night

the lord of the rings movies were made in new zealand

my favourite book is called the call of the wild

paul is leaving for paris tomorrow

rich requested that his mower be repaired by friday

Capital letters and fullstops – punctuating a story

Activities

These stories make no sense because they have no punctuation.

There are no capital letters or fullstops.

Put in the correct punctuation so that the stories make sense.

Story 1

my boyfriend and i went on a holiday to gran canaria we left on a sunday and returned the following saturday during our stay we saw a cricket match between tenerife and gran canaria island teams we also visited the loro park which was in a beautiful setting the dolphins were great in fact this was our favourite place in the park as well as this we went swimming off puerto de la cruz off a dive boat called sunfish it had two johnson engines on the dive trip there were people from the uk, us and germany it was a wonderful holiday

Story 2

i am trying to sell my car it is a 1999 mitsubishi suv with 4wd it has about 100,000 miles on it but is in very good shape i put an advert in the motor trade magazine that listed the price as £2500 ono the day it came out i had about six callers who were interested only one came to see it and he offered me £1500 for it but that wasn't enough i've decided that next tuesday i will take it to dan's auto auction on coronation avenue my friends tell me that the cars usually get good prices there

Story 3

when i went to work today my boss invited me into his office i was a bit nervous because i didn't know what he wanted to talk to me about he asked me to sit down and then told me what a good job i was doing since i started there last march he had looked at my cv and noticed that i had experience installing tvs, videos and dvd players he said that if i would do a course at a local college in electronics he would promote me to a new position of course i was thrilled and agreed i will start my course in april

Story 4

two of my friends and i have decided to train for the third annual triathlon being held in golden bay next november we are all over 40 so we will be in the sr class there will be swimming, cycling and running we don't care how we place because the important thing for us is that we finish we have been swimming laps at the bell block community pool twice a week on sundays we meet for a 5 kilometre bicycle ride we figure that with all that exercise we won't need to start training for the run for a few more weeks i wonder how we will do

Capital letters – summary
Capital letters are used for:

• names of people

Nelson Mandela
Jonah Lomu
Kylie Minogue
Albert Einstein

• the names of places

Rhyl
Wales
The Eiffel Tower
China

• the names of days

Tuesday
Wednesday
Thursday
Saturday

• the names of the months

January
February
April
September
November

• names of streets

Fifth Avenue
Towyn Road
Campbell Crescent

• names of businesses

Bank of Ireland, British Telecom
Powergen

• titles of books, magazines and newspapers

The Bible
The New York Times
The Listener

• initials

H. T. Black
VAT
HIV
RAC

© 2009 Aber Publishing – Adult Skills

Joined sentences

When writing it is easy to join sentences together with joining words such as **then**, **and**, **but**, **so** and **because**. The results of using a lot of joining words can be very long sentences.

Activities

Here are examples of stories that have a lot of joining words in them.

Improve the story by crossing out unneeded joining words, making corrections to capital letters and inserting fullstops.

Story 1

my sister anne asked me to babysit for her children drew and grant and they are 5 and 7 years old and i went to her house and decided to take them to the park then when they were ready to leave we couldn't find drew's shoes because he had taken them off to play in the sand but we looked all over and still couldn't find them anywhere and finally we had to go home without them and i was afraid that anne would be mad then she told me that the shoes he wore were getting too small anyway and not to worry so i didn't and she told me how much she appreciated me looking after the children then she gave me £20 and i told her that she didn't need to pay me but she insisted and i felt really pleased

Story 2

in february i started doing a certificate in horticulture at north wales college of horticulture and the course is one year long and on the first day the lecturer gave us a list of the reading we had to do and then she told us that we would have our first test on the following friday because this would help us to keep up with our reading and we also had to plan some field experience such as working at big jims garden centre for a commercial plant grower like duncan and davies or in an orchard picking fruit for the liverpool or manchester markets then she told us we would have to choose a research topic related to horticulture to do on the internet so i will certainly be very busy this year

Story 3

i work at brian and ralph investors and we had to move from one floor another because we were getting too crowded where we were and the next floor below us had a lot more space but i didn't want to give up my area because i had a lovely view of cardiff bay and enjoyed watching the sea and all the colours of the water and cloud formations but i knew there was no choice and packed my stuff in boxes and then took my turn at using the trolley to cart it down the elevator and into my new office and then i realised that not only did i have an office with a view of the bay but it was also next to the tearoom which i always visit frequently during the day and it wasn't such a bad move after all

© 2009 Aber Publishing – Adult Skills   Punctuation - Book 2

Question marks and exclamation marks

Capital letters and fullstops are common types of punctuation because they appear in most sentences.

There are two other punctuation marks that can be used in place of fullstops. They show that a sentence has ended but carry a different meaning than a fullstop.

These three punctuation marks can be used to end a sentence.

.	**The match starts at 8 pm.**	**Use a fullstop to show the end of a sentence.**
?	**When are we going to leave?**	**Use a question mark to show that a question has been asked.**
!	**If we win, we will be in the finals for the first time ever!**	**Use an exclamation mark to show something has been shouted, said strongly, excitedly or in surprise.**

Activity

Read each sentence. Put one of the punctuation marks at the end of each one.
Be prepared to explain your choice.

Watch out for that falling ladder

What are you getting your father for his birthday

Don't worry about bringing anything to the party

Be sure to let me know when the package arrives

When will you let me drive your new car

Jerry wants to start the climb up the mountain at 5 am

My purse disappeared at work today

Donna is expecting triplets in May

What colours are you going to choose for your wedding

Yesterday afternoon I finished the book I was reading

During the storm our power was out for eight hours

Please tell me what time you want your dinner to be ready

Do you prefer shopping at Asda or Woolworths

How many kilometres do you run each week

My uncle's farm was flooded and several cows drowned

I expect you to have the flat cleaned when I get home

Why are we having our Christmas party in November

The cricket team won the series against Pakistan

When are you going on your holiday

Question marks and exclamation marks

Activities

Read these stories. Insert the correct punctuation marks, including fullstops, question marks, exclamation marks and capital letters.

Cross out any joining words that aren't needed.

Story 1

one evening my mates and i were talking about going somewhere over the weekend but where should we go then after discussing it for a few minutes we decided to go hiking so we agreed that we would go to the quantocks in somerset

and the day of departure came and we gathered our gear which included backpacks, hiking boots, rain gear and sleeping bags but did we know anyone we could borrow a tent from and we could only find a 10-man size to borrow but we finally found a friend with a 4-man tent

so we met at my flat in newbury and drove down the m 4 to join the m5 to the south-west we stopped at services in bristol to get a coffee and something to eat then we drove on to bridgwater where we left the motorway and drove through the quantocks to our base in a village called bishops lydeard this was a beautiful village and we had lunch in the bell inn where the landlord dave made us very welcome in the afternoon we walked up the long hill and boy it was steep and went hiking into the hills here we saw deer and we readied our guns to shoot but dont worry these were not loaded with bullets these guns are a new style where instead of shooting bullets they shoot pictures they really look like guns but they have been adapted to be cameras so that day we got some really good shots of deer and the deer were not harmed

Story 2

last christmas was the first time i decided to get organised and make a list of the people i wanted to buy gifts for and what i wanted to buy everyone and how much i wanted to spend

so i wrote down all the names and then got adverts from stores and i looked through them and tried to find things that i thought everyone would like but could i afford all the things i wrote down

so i added up the totals to be sure i wasn't over my budget and i it was twice what i had to spend and it took me hours to redo my list

then i set aside one day in early december to go to each store and buy what i had written down and i was so surprised that i managed to get all my shopping done because in the past i was still shopping on christmas eve but when will i ever get all these presents wrapped

© 2009 Aber Publishing – Adult Skills   Punctuation - Book 2

Fullstops, question marks and exclamation marks – summary

A **sentence** is a word, or group of words, which makes sense on its own.

A **punctuation mark** is at the end of each sentence.

.

Fullstop

Tonight we are going to look through my new telescope.

I can see some people standing on the footpath.

I had to work last weekend to help meet a deadline.

?

Question mark

Would you like to look through my new telescope tonight?

Do you hear all those sirens?

Do you think I will get paid anything extra?

!

Exclamation mark

We saw three planets through my new telescope last night!

Two fire engines just stopped next door!

I got paid twice my normal hourly rate!

Speech marks

Speech marks are sometimes called **quotation marks**.

Why do we use speech marks?
In many stories, spoken words are written. Speech marks go at the beginning and end of spoken words to show the exact words that have been said.
Notice that each time a new person speaks, the words start on a new line.

Con said I should wait for her at the corner.	**These are not the exact words spoken by Con.**
Con said, "Wait for me at the corner."	**These are the exact words spoken by Con.**
Steve asked me if I would drive him home.	**These are not the exact words spoken by Steve.**
Steve asked, "Would you drive me home?"	**These are the exact words spoken by Steve.**

Activity 1

In this story, Gayle and Jim are speaking to each other. Underline only the words they actually say. The first one is done for you.

Gayle asked, <u>"Jim, do you want to go to the movies with me tonight?"</u>

Jim said he didn't want to go.

"Why don't you want to go?" prodded Gayle.

"Because I've seen the movie already," he admitted.

Gayle told him to choose another movie he wanted to see.

Jim replied, "I would rather hire a DVD and watch it at home."

After thinking about what he said, she admitted she'd rather stay home, too.

"Let's go and find a good fireside movie," she suggested. "How about that?"

Jim though for a while and chuckled, "How about Fire in the Sky?"

Activity 2

Circle all the speech marks. Are they at the beginning and the end of each of the underlines you drew?

Activity 3

Three sentences do not have speech marks. Rewrite them as if the person was speaking and correctly insert speech marks.

_____

_____

_____

Commas used with speech marks

In this example, a comma goes right *after* the words have been said and *before* the speech mark.

"Tomorrow we are all going surfing," Janet said.	The words Janet spoke are written first, and then *Janet said* was added at the end of the sentence.
	A comma is placed right *after* the spoken words.
	A fullstop is placed at the *end* of the sentence.

In this example, a comma goes *before* the speech marks and *before* the words that are spoken.

Matthew yelled, "Watch out for that truck!"	In this sentence, the speaker is mentioned first and then the words *Matthew spoke* are written.
	A comma is placed right *before* the spoken words and *before* the speech marks.
	An exclamation mark is placed at the *end* of the sentence.
"Tonight I'm going shopping. Would you like to go with me?" asked Susan.	When two or more sentences are spoken together, the speech marks are placed at the *end* of what was said.
"I would like to go to the races this weekend," said Dan. "I can't find anyone to go with me."	When two sentences are spoken by one person, but separated by words that are not spoken, speech marks are placed *before* and *after* the spoken words.

Activity

Put capital letters, speech marks, commas and other punctuation marks in the correct places in these sentences.

tomorrow we leave on our trip to australia said jill excitedly

are you all packed bill asked

jill said she wasn't and then went on to tell bill everything else she had to do

bill had a sceptical look on his face how are you going to get all that done

that is why i invited you over can you please bring my two large blue suitcases down from the attic jill asked nicely sure just as long as i don't have to fill them up admitted bill

A conversation

Activities

Study each of these photographs. Make up the people's names and write a conversation they might be having that goes with the photo.

Use all of the punctuation marks you have learned:

capital letters   .   ? !   ,   " "

1.

2.

Speech marks – summary

Speech marks go at the beginning and end of what a person says.

Use a comma after the words have been said:

"Let me know when you are ready to go," reminded Steph.

Use a comma after the speaker is mentioned.

Scott replied, "That will be in ten minutes."

When several people are speaking, each person's words are on a new line. When two or more sentences are spoken, the speech marks are placed at the beginning and end of what was said.

Mary agreed, "I'm ready, Scott. I'll wait at the car"

"Great," Scott said, pleased with her response.

"Hold on," said Steph.

When two sentences are spoken by one person, but separated by words that are not spoken, speech marks are placed before and after the spoken words.

"I'm worried about you, Steph." said Bill. "You don't sound very happy."

"I'm not", she admitted. "There's something important I have to do before we leave."

Using a question mark or exclamation mark with spoken words.

"How long will it take," Bill inquired, somewhat annoyed.

Steph asked "Just tell me why we have to leave so soon."

"The train is leaving in less than an hour!" Scott explained.

Commas – more uses

Commas are used

•   in speaking to separate what is said from who said it.

There are three more uses for commas.

CORRECT **I gathered my togs, towel, sandals and surf board to take to the beach.**	**A comma is used to separate items in a list.**
CORRECT **The sand was golden, fine, hot and blinding.**	**Commas are also used to separate lists of adjectives - words that describe something.**
NOT CORRECT **When I got home I was tired, sunburned, sore, and hungry.**	**A comma is not placed between the last item or adjective in the list, or after the words *and* and *or*.**
CORRECT **After doing all the housework, I just have to sit down and rest.**	**A comma is used to mark a place in a sentence to make you pause.**

Activities

1. Put the commas in these lists of items.

I put cereal bread milk biscuits sausages and butter on my shopping list.

Don't forget to take the baby's bottle blanket nappies and teddy bear to the babysitter's house.

For dinner do you want chicken ham fish steak or lamb?

In North Wales we saw Swallow Falls a castle the worm farm and took a ride on the lake.

Should we travel by car train or airplane?

2. Put the commas in these lists of adjectives.

She has many interesting bright attractive and single friends.

The trip was too long boring expensive and repetitive.

Ian doesn't want gifts for his birthday Christmas Father's Day or Valentine's Day.

The moon shimmered on the dark glassy lake.

3. Put the commas in these sentences where the reader should pause.

The more I get to know Frank the more I like him.

"You are a bad bad dog!"

The book which Jan gave me last night is very interesting.

The woman who mistook my coat for hers has returned it to me.

Commas – more uses

Commas are used:

* in writing to separate what is said from who said it,

* to separate lists of items,

* to separate lists of adjectives,

* to make the reader pause.

Commas are also used to give sentences meaning.

NOT CORRECT **A panda eats, shoots and leaves.**	**If a comma is put in the wrong place, a sentence can give the wrong meaning.**
CORRECT **A panda eats shoots and leaves.**	
NOT CORRECT **Mel is good at art with english and maths his worst subjects.**	**If a comma is left out, a sentence can also give a wrong or confusing meaning.**
CORRECT **Mel is good at art, with english and maths his worst subjects.**	

Activity

Remove or add commas in these sentences so that they are not confusing and give the meaning you think is correct.

My sister wearing a raincoat set, off in the storm.

Tim played the guitar Betty sang Zack, was on the drums and the crowd loved it.

Tomorrow will be very cold and rainy at times.

Athletes who seek their coach's advice often, can improve their game.

He was a short bearded fellow.

The nurse, examined the injured woman, lying on her back on the floor.

The doctor who wouldn't speak to, the patient had suspicions about his symptoms.

I thought until December, that I didn't have any leave left.

This house built, for the large family was finished, early.

Driving along the road in front of the fire station, I noticed a new ambulance.

The pond having been drained, and refilled numerous ducks returned.

When summer comes windsurfing, is a popular activity to watch.

From where we sat hearing the speaker was difficult.

Whichever one you select quickly pay for it and exit.

Comma – summary

Commas are used:

,

- **to separate what is said from who said it**

"What are you going to order?" asked Jay.

Chris replied, "I'll have the roast dinner, thanks."

,

- **to separate items in a list**

Let's get chocolate sauce, bananas and walnuts to go with our ice-cream.

,

- **to separate lists of adjectives**

On the mountain it was cold, snowy, slippery, icy and treacherous.

,

- **to mark a place in a sentence to make the reader pause**

My older sister, Betty, taught me how to drive.

,

- **to give sentences meaning**

When I give you the signal, make sure you start the car, drive down the street, pull up in the parking space beside the store and wait for me.

© 2009 Aber Publishing – Adult Skills   Punctuation - Book 2

Apostrophes – missing letters

Apostrophes can be used:

•   in place of a letter or letters to shorten or abbreviate words.

For example: *I am* can be shortened to *I'm*.

The apostrophe is placed where the letters are taken out.

Use the apostrophe to show that a letter has been left out of the word.

I have not read the book yet.	
I haven't read the book yet.	**The apostrophe replaces the *o* in *not*.**
We are leaving at 10 sharp.	
We're leaving at 10 sharp.	**The apostrophe replaces the *a* in *are*.**

Activity

Look at the words in these boxes. Put a circle around the letters in the left columns that have been removed from the words in the right columns.

Place the apostrophe in each shortened word to replace the letters that have been taken out.

I have	I ve		is not	isn t
we have	we ve		has not	hasn t
they have	they ve		have not	haven t
you have	you ve		cannot	can t
he is	he s		would not	wouldn t
she is	she s		should not	shouldn t
we are	we re		could not	couldn t
they are	they re		let us	let s
I will	I ll		I would	I d
we will	we ll		we would	we d
you will	you ll		you would	you d
they will	they ll		they would	they d

Apostrophes – possession

A second use of apostrophes is:

- to show that something belongs to one person or thing.

  For example: *That car belongs to Joe. = That is Joe's car.*

  The apostrophe goes before the s to show the car belongs to one person.

- to show that something belongs to more than one person or thing.

  For example: *These cats have many toys. = These are the cats' toys.*

  The apostrophe goes after the **s** to show the toys belong to more than one cat.

Use apostrophes to show possession.

Luke lost everything in the fire. Everything was lost in Luke's fire.	The apostrophe goes before the s because Luke is one person.
The tickets were bought by my sons. These are my sons' tickets.	The apostrophe goes after the s because there is more than one son.
The eggs are from those chickens. Those are the chickens' eggs.	The apostrophe goes after the s because there is more than one chicken.

Look at the pictures and ask yourself, "Who does it belong to?"

If it belongs to one person or thing, the apostrophe goes *before* the *s*.

If it belongs to more than one person or thing, the apostrophe goes *after* the *s*.

One person or thing.

Here is one person and a guitar.

This is the man's guitar.

More than one person or thing.

Here are some musicians with their instruments.

Here are the musicians' instruments.

Activity

Put the apostrophes in the correct places.

That is your mates car.

Are those your mates cars?

Listen to my new stereos surround sound.

My old and new stereos sounds are quite different.

Where are Glenns shoes?

That is your sisters cell phone.

Are those your sisters cell phones?

That slugs trail is making a mess on the carpet.

The slugs trails are making a mess on the carpet.

Jays car is red.

© 2009 Aber Publishing – Adult Skills   Punctuation - Book 2

Apostrophes – practice

Activity 1

Missing letters

1. On the line, write a word with an apostrophe.

I will	_____	be home late tonight.
He has	_____	saved enough to buy the car he wanted.
You have	_____	been invited to two parties in one night!
She is	_____	not able to come any sooner.
It would	_____	be better to eat before we go.
They would	_____	prefer steak to lamb.

2. Fill in the words in each blank that mean the same as the bold word on the left.

Let's	_____	_____	all enrol in the same course.
You'd	_____	_____	enjoy this album more than that one.
We've	_____	_____	just shifted into our new flat.
They're	_____	_____	planning to put up a new sign.
We'll	_____	_____	revise for the exam on Sunday night.

Activity 2

Possessives

3. On the line, write the underlined word with an apostrophe in the correct place.

My twin <u>brothers</u> birthday is on Monday. _____

My <u>brothers</u> birthday is on Monday. _____

The front <u>doors</u> lock is stuck. _____

The front and back <u>doors</u> locks are stuck. _____

Her <u>pens</u> cartridges have all run out of ink. _____

Her <u>pens</u> cartridge has run out of ink. _____

The office <u>telephones</u> ring is driving me crazy. _____

The office <u>telephones</u> rings are driving me crazy. _____

The <u>dockets</u> totals are all wrong. _____

The <u>dockets</u> total is all wrong. _____

His <u>mates</u> parents are meeting us at the café. _____

His <u>mates</u> mother is meeting us at the café. _____

His <u>mates</u> families are meeting us at the café. _____

© 2009 Aber Publishing – Adult Skills   Punctuation - Book 2

Apostrophe – summary

- An **apostrophe** is used to shorten two words to make one word.

  are not   aren't

- An **apostrophe** is put in where the letter(s) have been taken out.

  let us   let's

- An **apostrophe** is used to show that something belongs to someone or something.

  The kitten belongs to Sara.
  It is *Sara's* kitten.

- An **apostrophe** is used to show that something belongs to more than one person or thing.

  The paintings belong to the artists.
  They are the *artists'* paintings.

Here is one person and a guitar.
This is the man's guitar.

Here are some musicians with their instruments.

Here are the musicians' instruments.

Punctuation practice 1

. Use a **fullstop** at the end of all other sentences.

? Use a **question mark** in a sentence that asks a question.

! Use an **exclamation mark** in a sentence that is said strongly.

1. **Read the sentences below. For each sentence, write in one of the three punctuation marks above.**

When is the ferry expected

It doesn't matter if we're late

Watch out for that cricket ball

Yesterday was a lovely day

What are you going to name the puppies

For the last time, clean up your room

The racing car crashed into the fence and injured three people

How do you like your steak cooked

I'm supposed to get some training at work next week

What did you buy for your daughter's birthday

Is Mike coming to pick you up

I'll never eat hot peppers again

The wedding is going to be in the park

Which computer game do want to play

. Use a **fullstop** at the end of a complete sentence.

C Use a **capital** to start the names of people, places and days.
The word **I** is always a capital letter.

2. **Decide on the punctuation each sentence needs.**
For each sentence, write in one of the punctuation marks above.

i have always wanted to visit san Francisco

alison is babysitting her grandson this friday

my little sister loves the harry potter books

call in to the bank of ireland and pick up an application for me

we are going to see the new star wars movie at the valley cinema tonight

by july, the work on main street should be finished

we ate at the golden grill on wednesday

i can't wait for christmas when i'm going to hong kong

elvis presley sang jailhouse rock at the beginning of his career

we got our air france tickets from centre city travel

his brother just graduated from the university of loughborough

Punctuation practice 2

> **,** To separate lists of adjectives.
>
> **,** To mark a place in a sentence to make the reader pause.
>
> **,** To give sentences meaning.

1. Put the commas in the correct places in these sentences.

The falling leaves are creating carpets of orange yellow brown red and terracotta.

My favourite uncle is funny generous athletic and humble.

People like animals do not like to be held behind bars.

A few days later smiles became tears.

As soon as you bought your new flat houses became cheaper.

All the people who replied strongly agreed with the outcome.

Once they yelled timber immediately everyone ran.

> **" "**   Use **speech marks** around the words someone says.
>
> **,**   Use **commas** to separate what is said from who said it.

2. Insert or correct the punctuation in each sentence. Some sentences do not need correcting.

Hugh explained that the trip had been cancelled.

Close that door she pleaded The cold air is rushing in.

Connie yelled That bird just tried to dive-bomb me!

The crowd encouraged the performer to play an encore.

Mary mentioned that she had witnessed a car accident on her way to work.

Sue inquired Which car are you driving to North London?

I agree with what you admitted Joe but don't tell anyone

> **'**   An apostrophe is used to show that something belongs to something or someone.
>
> **'**   Use an apostrophe to show a letter has been left out of a word.

3. Write in the apostrophes in each sentence.
 I've been looking at Jans new van.
The suns rays are especially dangerous in the summer.
I know it's time to do the laundry when my dirty clothes basket is full.
All the boys shoes got muddy during the match.
Meet us at the theatres entrance at 6pm and we'll all go in together
That womans umbrella was turned inside out by the wind.
My students homework is due tomorrow.

Punctuation practice 3

In these stories there are a lot of missing punctuation marks. There are also too many ands, thens and buts. Make all the corrections and then copy the story on a separate page.

Story 1

lets go bike riding suggested tina it is a warm beautiful day

shouldnt we take along something to eat leo asked

thats a good idea why dont you bring drinks and ill bring sandwiches apples and chips and some biscuits

tina and leo decided to meet at 10 at leos house at 9:30 tina rang leo and told him that her brothers friend had borrowed her bike and she couldnt go but leo assured her that she could use his sisters bike and tina was very pleased about this

on their way to the beach they noticed that there were a lot of roadworks going on their wheels were throwing up chippings and so they decided to take a shortcut through the alley behind their neighbours houses and all of a sudden they saw a person running from the back of a yard carrying some of the houses contents under his arms

stop shouted leo but the burglar didnt stop

leo and tina followed the thief on their bikes nearly running him over and he finally stopped when he got tired and dropped the stolen items and ran away

tina rang the police on her cell phone to explain what had happened and they had to wait half an hour for the police to come and when they did they explained what they had seen and gave them a description of the person they saw they didnt get to the beach until noon but at least it was in time for their picnic

Story 2

travelling in an airplane for the first time i didnt know my way around at all and i wasnt even sure where my seat was so i asked one of the cabin crew which side of the plane is my seat on and they showed me then i saw that there was an overhead compartment for my carryon laptop and book and put them in it

later after the meal i needed to use the loo and there was no crew to ask and so i walked around and found it myself and was i checked one of the doors locks and saw that it was vacant

and i walked up the aisle to return to my seat can i help you someone asked from behind me im just going back to my seat im sorry but you have come into the first class passengers section by mistake i was so embarrassed and it seemed that all the passengers eyes were on me no worries said the hostess just turn around and you will find your seat righto i said and i did an about-face and found my empty seat

at the end of the flight i collected my things and thought what an interesting and embarrassing and fun plane trip this had been my family met me and we laughed about my mistake one day i hope i will get to travel first class for real but until then ill make sure i stay in the correct part of the plane

Story 1

Let's go bike riding, suggested Tina. It is a warm, beautiful day."

"Shouldn't we take along something to eat?" Leo asked.

"That's a good idea. Why don't you bring drinks? I'll bring sandwiches, apples, chips and some biscuits."

Tina and Leo decided to meet at 10 at Leo's house. At 9:30 Tina rang Leo and told him that her brother's friend had borrowed her bike and she couldn't go. Leo assured her that she could use his sister's bike. Tina was very pleased about this.

On their way to the beach, they noticed that there were a lot of roadworks going on. Their wheels were throwing up chippings, so they decided to take a shortcut through the alley behind their neighbours' houses. All of a sudden, they saw a person running from the back of a yard carrying some of the house's contents under his arms.

Stop!" shouted Leo, but the burglar didn't stop.

Leo and Tina followed the thief on their bikes, nearly running him over. He finally stopped when he got tired, dropped the stolen items and ran away.

Tina rang the police on her cell phone to explain what had happened. They didn't get to beach until noon, but at least it was in time for their picnic.

Story 2

Travelling in an airplane for the first time, I didn't know my way around at all. I wasn't even sure where my seat was, so I asked one of the cabin crew, "Which side of the plane is my seat on?" They showed me. I saw that there was an overhead compartment for my carryon, laptop and book, and put them in it.

Later, after the meal, I needed to use the loo. There was no crew to ask, and so I walked around and found it myself. I checked one of the door's locks and saw that it was vacant.

Afterwards, I walked up the aisle to return to my seat.

"Can I help you?" someone asked from behind me.

"I'm just going back to my seat."

"I'm sorry, but you have come into the first class passengers' section by mistake!"

I was so embarrassed! It seemed that all the passengers' eyes were on me.

"No worries," said the hostess. "Just turn around and you will find your seat."

"Righto," I said. I did an about-face and found my empty seat.

At the end of the flight I collected my things and thought what an interesting, embarrassing, and fun plane trip this had been. My family met me and we laughed about my mistake.

One day I hope I will get to travel first class for real! But until then, I'll make sure I stay in the correct part of the plane.

HAVERING COLLEGE OF F & H E

207711